FUN FAX
BRAIN TEASERS

Compiled by The Puzzle House

Henderson Publishing

Woodbridge, England

1 | STARTER

In 1999 how many months will have 28 days in them?

2 | SEEING'S BELIEVING

Using your eyes only can you decide which is the longer — the distance from A to B or from C to D?

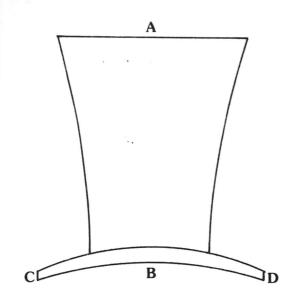

Answers to all puzzles can be found at the back of this book, starting on page 40.

3 | PET SHOP

The name of a type of creature that you could find in a pet shop is hidden in each of the sentences below. Make the names by joining together words or parts of words.

1 He is a bit of a do-gooder.
   ANSWER: DOG

2 All the fabric attaches to the curtain rail.
   ANSWER: _Cat_

3 In anger, Bill tore up the paper!
   ANSWER: _GERBILL_

4 It was a below par, rotten game!
   ANSWER: _PARROT_

5 I'm sure that the crab bit my ankle!
   ANSWER: _RABBIT_

4 | NAME GAME

In this puzzle each letter of the alphabet has been given a numerical value. The value of each name is reached by adding the individual numbers together.

$$A \, V \, A \; = 4$$
$$D \, A \, L \, E \; = 19$$
$$D \, A \, V \, E \; = 15$$
$$E \, V \, A \; = 11$$

What is D E L L A worth?

5 | CATCHER

There is a word of five letters from which you can take two away and leave one. Do you know what it is?

Friendly warning . . . if you think there's a catch in this, you're right!

6 | BOGGLERS

What does this mean? **BA-NA-NA**. No problems, it's BANANA SPLIT, of course. Look out for other BOGGLERS as they appear throughout this book . . . starting with this one . . .

<u>THE WEATHER</u>
FEELING

7 | GROANER!

Which are the most intelligent letters of the alphabet?

8 | LOG-PIC

Look at the pictures and the things people say. Try to work out the names of the children — 1 to 4 — and the dogs — A to D. Then match dogs to their owners.

1   I'M CALLED ALAN. MY DOG HAS BLACK EARS.   B

JULIE'S DOG ROVER HAS BLACK EARS.   2

A

3   I'M CALLED LYNNE.

C   THIS IS FANG

SCAMP   D   TOWSER IS THE DOG BELONGING TO MALCOLM.   4

9 | STOP GAP

Using only one word to each group, fill in the gaps in the given words.

1   M _ _ _ E T

     D _ _ _

     P _ _ _ I N G

2   S E A _ _ _

     _ _ _ G

     R E A _ _ _

3   C A R _ _ _

     _ _ _ R O L

     _ _ _ A L

10 | WHAT'S NEXT?

What should come next in this sequence?

     M   T   W   T   F   S   _

11 | GOOD GARDENING

A gardener has FIVE days in which to plant out 200 flower beds. All the beds are the same shape and size.

The gardener starts off slowly, but he picks up speed and finishes his planting in the five day deadline. Each day he planted out TWELVE more beds than on the previous day.

So how many beds did he plant out on the first day?

12 RIDDLE-ME-REE

I went to America and stopped there.
I came back as I didn't go there.
What am I?

13 SKELETON

We've provided the skeleton framework of a crossword and you have to complete the job! Use the listed words along with as many black squares as you choose to complete the frame in which words will read either across or down.

3 Letters
AIR   ARK   EAR   EMU
JAM   NET   SKY   SUN   TOP

4 Letters
DAYS   HUNT   TREE   YOKE

5 Letters
NANNY   OTTER

9 Letters
FANTASTIC   TRANSPORT   WEDNESDAY

W	E	D	N	E	S	D	A	Y
				■				
			■	T				
				O				
				P				

14 JUMBO PROBLEM

What do elephants have that no other animals have?

15 BROKEN COUPLES

Some words go together — like FISH and CHIPS. Each pair of words below is linked together, but we've rearranged the letters to make things difficult for you. Try to work out what all the words should be.

1 HACS AND RAYCR

2 SHAMS AND BRAG

3 EDHI AND EKES

4 COYBOWS AND SNIDIAN

5 FORPIT AND SOLS

6 TILTLE AND GLARE

16 BOGGLERS

What does this boggler mean?

S

E

I

R

D

17 CENTURY

Move from START to FINISH going through linked boxes, and find a route in which the numbers you collect add up to exactly 100.

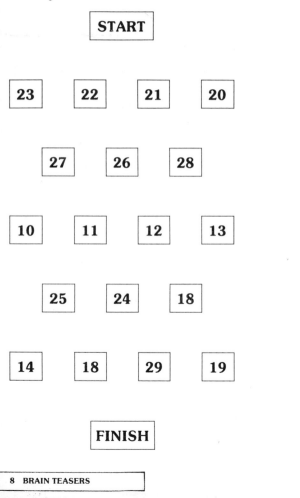

START

| 23 | 22 | 21 | 20 |

| 27 | 26 | 28 |

| 10 | 11 | 12 | 13 |

| 25 | 24 | 18 |

| 14 | 18 | 29 | 19 |

FINISH

18 RIDE ON

A word square reads the same whether you look at it across or down. Here's an example.

F	I	S	H
I	S	L	E
S	L	I	M
H	E	M	S

Use the listed words to make THREE different word squares. Use every word once, with RIDE appearing in each word square.

ADAM	DEAR	EARL
FURS	IDEA	MEMO
PRAM	RIDE	RIDE
RIDE	STEM	UNIT

19 SEEING'S BELIEVING

Using your eyes only, can you say which is the longer, the line of the T going up, or the line going across?

20 TEAMWORK

This is the final table after a soccer tournament involving four teams. All sides played each other once. There were three points for a win, one point for a draw, and no points for a defeat.

What was the score in the game between City and Rovers?

	P	Won	Drew	Lost	Goals For	Goals Against	Points
ROVERS	3	2	1	0	4	1	7
UNITED	3	2	0	1	3	1	6
RANGERS	3	0	2	1	0	2	2
CITY	3	0	1	2	1	4	1

21 WHICH WINDOW?

Picture A shows the view from INSIDE a room looking OUT. The numbered pictures show the OUTSIDE of the building looking IN through the window. Only one picture matches with picture A . . . which window is it?

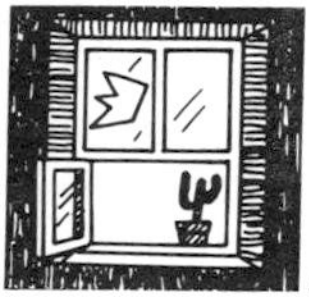
A

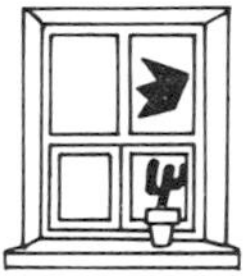
1

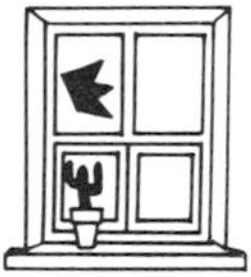
2

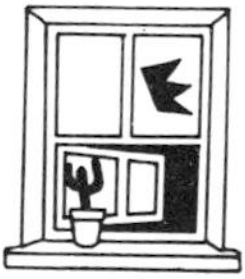
3

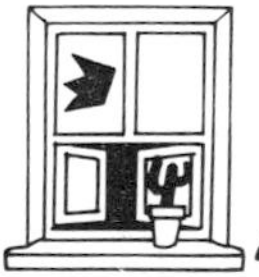
4

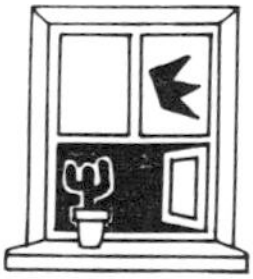
5

22 WHAT AM I?

Use the clues in the rhyme to work out what I am. The answer is something that most of us find very useful!

My first is in make
But isn't in cake.
My second is in broke
But isn't in brake.
My third is in bank
But isn't in back.
My fourth is in trace
But isn't in track.
My fifth is in try
But isn't in tree.
Have you worked out
What I could be?

23 BLACK ADDER

This is a straight-forward sum . . . or rather it would have been if we hadn't replaced the numbers with letters!

The numbers represented in the sum are 0 to 5. Can you work out the answer to the sum in numbers?

```
A   C   D   B   C   +

C   E   D   B   D
_____

F   B   A   D   C
```

24 BOGGLERS

What does the boggler mean?

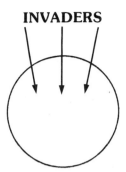

INVADERS

25 AFTER YOU

Which word can go after all of these to make new words?

HAT

HAND

GRAND

BAND

26 CODED

This is a coded crossword. The letters have been taken out and replaced by numbers. See if you can crack the code and work out all the words.

All 26 letters of the alphabet appear in the crossword, and we've given you a start by writing one word in place. So, each time you see a number 1 put an S in the square, a number 2 means write in a T, a number 3 means write in an R, and so on.

7	4	3	8	17		1	14	4	25	7
8			4		18		4			16
7		¹S	²T	³R	⁴A	⁵N	⁶G	⁷E		2
15	4	14	7		19		7	13	7	3
2		4		7	7	8		7		4
	20	3	10	6		10	9	5	1	
21		3		6	7	2		12		24
22	14	10	5		15		23	5	7	7
12		9	4	1	11	12	5	6		4
7			12		10		7			5
2	4	26	8	7		1	9	4	5	1

1	2	3	4	5	6	7	8	9	10	11	12	13
S	T	R	A	N	G	E						

14	15	16	17	18	19	20	21	22	23	24	25	26
A	B	C	D	E	F	G	H	I	J	K	L	M
N	O	P	Q	R	S	T	U	V	W	X	Y	Z

Use these grids to help you solve the puzzle.

27 ALPHASTEP

Each clue has two answers. The second answer is spelt the same as the first, except that the initial letter has stepped forward one place in the alphabet.

So for example, if answer one was BAT the second answer would be CAT. Got the idea? Try these.

1   Ship, sailing vessel * Article of clothing to wear over your normal clothes when you go out.

    ANSWERS: _____

2   Belongs to me   *   Number of lives of a cat.

    ANSWERS: _____

3   Tear to pieces   *   Take in small amount of a drink

    ANSWERS: _____

4   Time when prices are reduced in shops   *   A story

    ANSWERS: _____

5   Type of door in a garden hedge or fence   *   Strong dislike

    ANSWERS: _____

28 WHAT'S NEXT?

What should come next in this sequence?

1   2   5   10   20   50   _____

29 COLUMNS

COLUMN A	COLUMN B	COLUMN C
1		
2		
		3
	4	
	5	
6		
		7
		8
	9	

In which column should 10 go? There is a reason behind each number going in each column, and 10 must follow the same pattern when you place it. It's a tricky one but we aren't going to spell out the answer.

30 MISSING FACES

There are three people who appear in picture A who do NOT appear in picture B. Can you identify the missing faces?

31 NAME DROPPING

Complete the words below by dropping a boy's name into the spaces. Use the same name for all the words in the same group.

1   P A R _ _ _

     _ _ _ A T I O N

     C O N _ _ _ E

2   _ _ _ I D

     _ _ _ B E R

     _ _ _ E

3   _ _ _ P L E

     _ _ _ B A

     _ _ _ A R I T A N

32 BOGGLERS

What does the boggler mean?

     HEAVY

     HEAVY

33 AWKWARD

The Really Awkward Society is about to meet. There are FOUR different groups, the North, South, East and West. As you might expect, they are so awkward that it is hard to fix a month to get together. The complaints are:

1   The Northern group don't want a meeting in a month that has an even number of letters in its name, the only exception being June.

2   The Southern group don't want a month that ends with the letters B,E,R.

3   The Eastern group don't want a month with exactly 30 days in it.

4   The Western group don't want a month whose first letter is the same as any other month.

Now this rules out ALL the months of the year. So to be really awkward, the society agrees to hold its meeting in the month which has MOST objections against it.

Which month is it?

34 FIX THE SIX

Solve the answers to the clues, then fit the SIX letter words back in the grid. Write answers in the spaces round the matching numbers. But which way do they go . . . clockwise or anti-clockwise?

We've given a one letter start, then you have to decide the direction of the words.

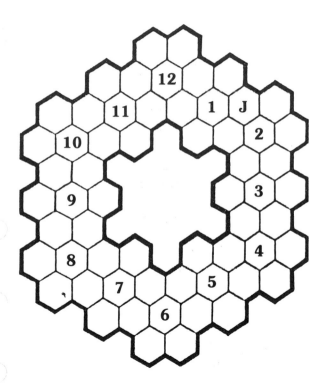

1   Person who runs gently for exercise

   ___ ___ ___ ___ ___ ___

2   Person who rides a horse in a race

   ___ ___ ___ ___ ___ ___

3   Container with a handle used to carry water

   ___ ___ ___ ___ ___ ___

4   Dancing performed on the toes

   ___ ___ ___ ___ ___ ___

5   Something to use to climb up

   ___ ___ ___ ___ ___ ___

6   The same again in size

   ___ ___ ___ ___ ___ ___

7   Places to live

   ___ ___ ___ ___ ___ ___

8   Suddenly go a-a-atchoooo!

   ___ ___ ___ ___ ___ ___

9   Plant and animal life

   ___ ___ ___ ___ ___ ___

10   Poultry traditionally served at Christmas and also the name of a country

   ___ ___ ___ ___ ___ ___

11   It covers the organ of sight

   ___ ___ ___ ___ ___ ___

12   Something built across a river to let you go over it

   ___ ___ ___ ___ ___ ___

35 HOME TIME

Time to head for home and that's what
Alan, Belinda, Christine and Dave want to
do. Here's a view looking down on the
blocks of buildings near their homes. We've
shown where the children are and where
their houses can be found . . . but which
route will they take?

The children must NOT meet on their
journeys, nor must their paths cross.
Which way did they all go?

36 ADD WORD

B   BR   GR   L   S   ST

What three-letter word can be added on to all of these to make new words?

37 NEWSDAY

D A Y = 6

S U N D A Y = 28

T U E S D A Y = 28

W E D N E S D A Y = 43

The nine letters that make up the words above have been given numerical values from 1 to 9. The total is arrived at by adding together the individual value given to the letters. The code stays the same, so if D was worth 9 in one word it would be worth 9 in all other words.

Using the same rules what would be the total of N E W S D A Y ?

38 BOGGLERS

What does the boggler mean?

BECOME

CONFIDENT

39 RIDDLE-ME-REE

In what game can you jump over three men without bothering to get up?

40 WHAT'S NEXT?

What should come next in this sequence?

41 DOMINOES

Can you replace the dominoes back into the shape shown here. The double six and double blank are positioned. The rules of an ordinary game of dominoes apply, with touching numbers being the same and doubles placed differently to dominoes that have two numbers on them.

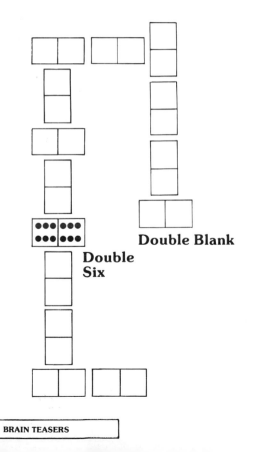

Double Blank

Double Six

42 SPACE INVADERS

Three Martian delegates and three Venusians attend a galactic conference. All SIX of them must travel from their spacecraft to the meeting place. Transport from the main spacecraft is by a two-seater space shuttle.

The Venusians distrust the men from Mars and insist that on no occasion can the Martians outnumber the Venusians. (Sounds like 'Neighbours').

How many times must the shuttle make the journey from the spacecraft to the meeting place and back again so that the Venusians are kept happy?

43 BOGGLERS

What does the boggler mean?

```
    G           G
 G  O        G  O
 N  I        N  I
```

44 DOUBLE TAKE

Answer each clue with a five-letter word, so that the last two letters of one answer will be the same as the first two of the next answer. The middle row reading down also forms a word. What is it?

1 Person on the other side
2 Describes someone who is distant from others, a bit stand-offish
3 Happens many times
4 Describes the people who you fight against in a war
5 One of the gifts from the Wise Men to the baby Jesus

1 <u>R</u>_ _ _ _

2 _ _ _ _ _

3 _ _ _ _ _

4 _ _ _ _ _

5 _ _ _ _ _

45 THE E'S HAVE IT

Simply count all the E's in the following sentence . . . it's as EEE'sy as that.

> Each Easter every exiled Englishman entertains endless entreaties for exotic eggs.

46 FITBACK

Fit the listed words back into the frame. There's a one word start and there's only one possible solution.

3 Letters
ACE ACT ASK EMU

4 Letters
COOL ROOM SOLD STAR

5 Letters
FINCH SPEND STEEP TABBY

6 Letters
CAMERA EXCUSE

7 Letters
CULPRIT SUCCESS

8 Letters
SCOTTISH SHOELACE

9 Letters
CONSTABLE IMPORTANT

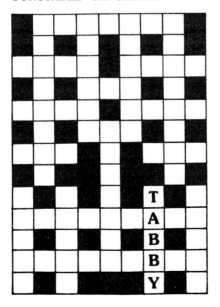

47 IN THE BAG

There are six buns and a bag. You give six children a bun each and find that you're not left with an empty bag.

Why not?

48 MEAN MENU

Here's a real mean menu. Numbers have taken the place of letters. Given that each number always stands for the same letter, can you work out the food that's on offer?

Starter

    1 2 3 4

Main Course

    5 6 2 3 5

Vegetables

    1 4 6 2 3 5 1

    4 2 5 7 5 2 8 1

Sweet

    1 9 6 3 4   5 7 6 5

49 SEEING'S BELIEVING

Using your eyes only, can you decide whether the white bars are straight, or do they bulge and bend?

50 GOOD'N'BAD

The Good family have three boys, Tom, Dick and Harry. The Bad family also have three boys called Tom, Dick and Harry.

The Good family ALWAYS tell the truth.

The BAD family always lie.

Three of the boys are playing together. Two of them are Bads and the other is a Good. The names of the lads are Tom, Dick and Harry . . . but which family do they belong to?

Try and work it out given this information:

Boy 1 said that his name was not Dick.

Boy 2 said his name was not Tom.

Boy 3 said his name was Tom.

51 WET, WET, WET

Which letter stands for the ocean?

52 FIGURE IT OUT

Using the figures 3, 4, 6 and 8 and without repeating a used number, can you decide what number should appear in the final space?

4638	6843	3864	4863
6483	8364	3648	6348
4386	6438	8643	3486
4368	3468	6834	4683
6384	8634	4836	8463
3846	8436	8346	????

53 MOVE THE MIDDLE

There are two answers to each clue. Both words are spelt the same, except that the middle letter is different. HAT and HOT forms an example.

1 Neck garment   *   Part of the foot
   ANSWERS: _____
2 Bark of large dog   *   Child not a girl
   ANSWERS: _____
3 Used to play cricket   *   Chewed into
   ANSWERS: _____
4 Female sheep   *   Used to see with
   ANSWERS: _____
5 N. American elk   *   Code for sending signals
   ANSWERS: _____

54 BOGGLERS

What does the boggler mean?

CAKE

55 SHAPE UP

There is something rather strange that
links together all the listed words. It has
nothing to do with the meanings. Have a
look at them and see if you can shape up to
finding an answer.

WAX   TOMATO
MOTTO   HAT
TOOTH   HOT

56 LOG-PIC

Look at the pictures and the things people
say. Try to work out the names of the
children — 1 to 4 — and match them to
their musical instruments — A to D.

57 RIDDLE-ME-REE

What can go up a chimney down but can't come down a chimney up?

58 RAINBOW'S END

Hidden in each of the sentences below is a colour of the rainbow. Find the hidden colours by joining together words or parts of words.

1   The girl and boy are definitely not here.

ANSWER: _____

2   Let us both agree not to say a single thing.

ANSWER: _____

3   I can still hear the music of the viol, ethereal and haunting.

ANSWER: _____

4   Keep calm, or anger will betray us.

ANSWER: _____

5   It was a shindig of the old-fashioned type.

ANSWER: _____

59 TWISTER

Write down FIVE odd numbers which you can use to make a total of 20. You might say there's a twist in this one!

60 BOX FOX

Take FOUR letter A's.
Take THREE letter B's.
Take THREE letter C's.
Take THREE letter D's.
Take THREE letter E's.

Now try to put them back into the box of
letters so that none of the same letters are
next to each other or appear together in
the same diagonal letter line in the box.
Four letters are in place to start you off.

B		E	
C			
D			

61 SEEING'S BELIEVING

Using your eyes only, can you say which of
the figures has the longest sides?

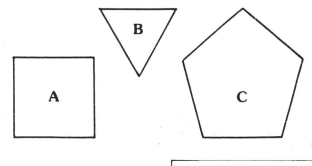

62 SOAPY

Mrs Savitt is in charge of making sure that the boys and girls wash-basins always have bars of soap in them. She's discovered that the children always leave a little piece of soap behind when they ask for a new bar. Thrifty Mrs Savitt started collecting the 'left-overs' and found that they could be stuck together to make new bars of soap. Every seven left-over bits will make another bar of soap.

She buys a pack containing 49 new bars of soap. Counting the bars she puts together, how many bars of soap will she have in total?

63 LINX

What's the link between all these words? It has nothing to do with the meanings. Study the words carefully and see if you can come up with a solution.

GOLF

TRAP

REWARD

WAR

FLOW

SAW

64 PLOT THE PLOTS

Using just FOUR straight lines divide this land into NINE plots, so that each plot contains a house, two trees and one cow.

65 COLOUR CODED

By substituting numbers in place of letters, we've disguised the names of certain colours. Can you crack the code and work out the colours. Perhaps the word with three numbers — and, of course, three letters — would be a good place to start.

1 2 3 3 4 5   — — — — — —

6 7 2 2 8   — — — — —

7 2 10   — — —

4 7 9 8 6 2   — — — — — —

11 7 4 5 8   — — — — —

66 ANIMAL CRACKERS

The names of which animals are made up of just two letters, with both letters being the same!!!

67 BOGGLERS

What does the boggler mean?

HEAVENS

_____

68 SQUARE DEAL

A word square reads the same whether you look at it across or down. Use the twelve listed words to make THREE word squares, using all the words and with CODE appearing in each square.

ANON	CODE	CODE	CODE
DISC	DOLL	EELS	INTO
JACK	KNEW	OBOE	STUD

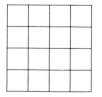

69 JUMBLIE

Take a pair of 6's, a pair of 7's, a pair of 8's and a pair of 9's. These can be put together to make a number containing eight digits, in which the 6's are separated by one digit, the 7's by two digits, the 8's by three digits and the 9's by four digits. If the last digit is a 9, what is the number?

70 PIC-TRICK

These six pictures will tell a story when they are put back in the correct order. What order is it?

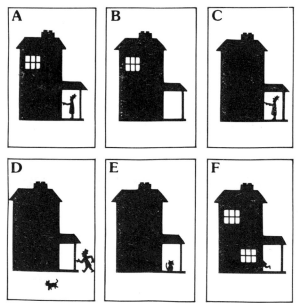

71 BIRD BRAINS

Fill in the blanks with the names of birds.
The first one is done to start you off.

1 C <u>R O O K</u> E D

2 S C _ _ _

3 A F _ _ _ _ O O N

4 B _ _ _ _ _

5 _ _ _ _ C H

6 _ _ _ _ _ O U S

72 BAD ADD

ONE + TWELVE = THIRTEEN
So far so good . . . but now try to rearrange
the letters in TWELVE and ONE to spell
out another two numbers which still add up
to THIRTEEN.

_____ + _____ = THIRTEEN

73 A TRIFLE TRICKY

At a party, Mum knows that three of the children— Debbie, Jim and Mick — have a particular pud which they really like. The sweets are cake, jelly and trifle, but Mum can't remember which likes which.

To make matters worse, Mum knows the three kids have the surname Brown, Black and White . . . but again she doesn't know which is which.

Fortunately, Dad remembers that, "Jim likes trifle." Gran remembers that, "The White girl doesn't like cake, and I wouldn't bother about Mick Black . . . he's always late."

That information was enough for Mum to work out first name to surname and match them with their favourite afters. Can you do the same?

74 EVENING ALL

How do you make 7 even?

ANSWERS

1. Starter
All of them. Some have more than 28, but they all have 28 days in them.
2. Seeing's Believing
The distance A to B is exactly the same as C to D. (Measure them out if you don't believe it!)
3. Pet Shop
1 Dog 2 Cat 3 Gerbil 4 Parrot 5 Rabbit
4. Name Game
DELLA = 25. E = 8, L = 6, D = 4, V = 2, A = 1
5. Catcher
STONE. Take away two letters (S and T) to leave ONE.
6. Bogglers
Feeling under the weather
7. Groaner!
Y's. Sounds like WISE. (Groan!)
8. Log-Pic
1 Alan C Fang. 2 Malcolm A Towser.
3 Lynne D Scamp. 4 Julie B Rover.
9. Stop Gap
1 Ark 2 Son 3 Pet
10. What's Next?
S. They are the first letters of the days in the week.
11. Good Gardening
On the first day he planted out 16 beds. On day two he managed 28, day 3 was 40, day 4 was 52 and day 5 was 64.
16 + 28 + 40 + 52 + 64 = 200.
12. Riddle-Me-Ree
A watch

13. Skeleton

W	E	D	N	E	S	D	A	Y
	M		E		K		R	
H	U	N	T		Y	O	K	E
		A		J		T		
F	A	N	T	A	S	T	I	C
		N		M		E		
D	A	Y	S		T	R	E	E
	I		U		O		A	
T	R	A	N	S	P	O	R	T

14. Jumbo Problem
Baby elephants!

15. Broken couples
1 Cash and carry 2 Smash and grab 3 Hide and seek 4 Cowboys and Indians 5 Profit and loss 6 Little and large

16. Bogglers
Dries up

17. Century
21 26 11 24 18

18. Ride on

P	R	A	M
R	I	D	E
A	D	A	M
M	E	M	O

R	I	D	E
I	D	E	A
D	E	A	R
E	A	R	L

F	U	R	S
U	N	I	T
R	I	D	E
S	T	E	M

19. Seeing's Believing
The line going up and the line going across are the same length.

20. Teamwork

Rovers beat City by 3 goals to 1. Rangers drew 2 games and as they didn't score a single goal, these must have been 0-0 results. United didn't draw, so the games had to be against Rovers and City. United were the team to beat Rangers, 2-0 is the only possible score. As United won another game and lost another the scores in both those games had to be both 1-0. So, Rovers have so far drawn 1 (0-0) and won 1 (1-0). To reach their final goals tally, they have to beat City by 3-1.

No action replay on this solution!

21. Which Window?
No 5

22. What am I?
Money

23. Black Adder
Answer is 45, 103. A = 1, B = 5, C = 3, D = 0, E = 2, F = 4

24. Bogglers
Space invaders

25. After you
Stand

26. Coded

27. Alphastep
1 Boat Coat 2 Mine Nine 3 Rip Sip 4 Sale Tale
5 Gate Hate

28. What's Next
1. They are coins. The 1 is for a one pound coin

29. Columns
Column A. The numbers have been arranged
according to the number of letters when they
are spelt out as words. (There was a good clue
to set you in the right direction)

30. Missing Faces

31. Name Dropping
1 Don 2 Tim 3 Sam

32. Bogglers
Too heavy

33. Awkward
November

34. Fix the Six
1 Jogger 2 Jockey 3 Bucket 4 Ballet 5 Ladder
6 Double 7 Houses 8 Sneeze 9 Nature
10 Turkey 11 Eyelid 12 Bridge

35. Home Time

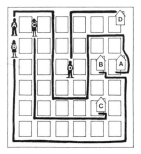

36. Add Word
And. Band, Brand, Grand, Land, Sand, Stand.
37. Newsday
NEWSDAY = 35. N = 9, E = 5, W = 8, S = 7,
DAY = 6
38. Bogglers
Become over confident
39. Riddle-Me-Ree
Draughts

40. What's Next?

41. Dominoes

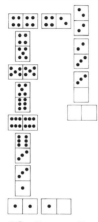

42. Space Invaders
6 journeys. 1. Martian and Venusian travel out, the Venusian returns. 2. Two M's out, one M returns. 3. Two V's out, one V and one M return. 4. Two V's out, one M returns. 5. Two M's travel out, one M returns. 6. Two M's travel together.

43. Bogglers
Going round in circles

44. Double Take
1 Rival 2 Aloof 3 Often 4 Enemy 5 Myrrh.
VOTER

45. The E's Have It
17

46. Fitback

47. In the Bag

Give the last child the bun which is still in the bag.

48. Mean Menu

Starter: SOUP Main Course: TROUT
Vegetables: SPROUTS, POTATOES Sweet: SYRUP TART

49. Seeing's Believing

White bars are straight. Black lines give the illusion the white bars start to bend.

50. Good'n'bad

Boy 1 is Harry Good. Boy 2 is Tom Bad. Boy 3 is Dick Bad.

51. Wet, Wet, Wet

C. (Sea)

52. Figure it out

3684

53. Move the Middle

1 Tie Toe 2 Bay Boy 3 Bat Bit 4 Ewe Eye
5 Moose Morse

54. Bogglers

Upside-down cake

55. Shape up
The letters are the link in this puzzle. Every letter is a 'mirror' image. The right section mirrors the left section.

56. Log-Pic
1 Pete D Recorder 2 Dawn A Piano
3 Geoff B Guitar 4 Kathy C Drum

57. Riddle-Me-Ree
Umbrella

58. Rainbow's End
1 Red 2 Green 3 Violet 4 Orange 5 Indigo

59. Twister
9 + 9 + 9 + 1 + 1. Turn it upside down . . . that's the twist. Now reads 1 + 1 + 6 + 6 + 6

60. Box Fox
B A E C
C D B A
A E C D
D B A E

61. Seeing's Believing
All the same

62. Soapy
57. 49 in the box. The 49 left-over bits make 7 new bars THEN the 7 new bars will leave left-overs to make another bar.

63. Linx
All the words form different words when read backwards.

64. Plot the plots

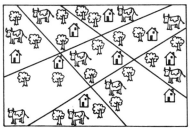

65. Colour Coded
Yellow, Green, Red, Orange, Brown
66. Animal Crackers
UU (Ewes) !!!
67. Bogglers
Heavens Above!
68. Square Deal

C	O	D	E
O	B	O	E
D	O	L	L
E	E	L	S

J	A	C	K
A	N	O	N
C	O	D	E
K	N	E	W

D	I	S	C
I	N	T	O
S	T	U	D
C	O	D	E

69. Jumblie
78,976,869
70. Pic-Trick
E-D-C-A-F-B
71. Bird Brains
1 Rook 2 Owl 3 Tern 4 Eagle 5 Wren 6 Raven
72. Bad Add
ELEVEN and TWO
73. A Trifle Tricky
Debbie White likes jelly. Jim Brown likes trifle.
Mick Black likes cake.
74. Evening All
Take away the letter S. S(EVEN)

More FUNFAX Titles

Fascinating Lists   **Essential Facts**
Brain Teasers   **Pocket Puzzler**
How it Works   **Living World**
Book of Crosswords   **How to Draw Cartoons**
Teenage Mutant Hero Turtles' Awesome Puzzler
Teenage Mutant Hero Turtles' Radical Fun Book
Beginner's Guide to French
Ghosts, Monsters and Legends
Jokes, Jokes and More Jokes
Beginner's Guide to Magic
Picture Puzzles **Fast Food** **The Turbulent Triangle**
A 'Spot-it' Guide to Nature

For a full list of FUNFAX titles, please write to the publishers enclosing a stamped addressed envelope.

SPECIAL OFFER

FUNFAX ORGANISER

Collect six different vouchers — there is one printed on the inside back cover of each book — send them to us with a cheque in the sum of £4.49 and we will send you a **Funfax Organiser** at the Special Offer price of £3.99 (plus 50 pence towards postage and packing). This represents a big saving on normal prices.

Send the coupon below to Henderson Publishing Ltd, P.O. Box 19, Woodbridge, Suffolk, IP12 4LT.

Offer available in UK only.

------------------------✂------------------------

Funfax Organiser: Yes, I would like to take advantage of the above special offer. I enclose six different vouchers (one voucher per title) and a cheque/postal order to the value of £4.49, made payable to Henderson Publishing Ltd. Please send me the Funfax Organiser. Please print in BLOCK LETTERS

NAME ....

ADDRESS..

....

Allow 28 days for delivery.

VOUCHER/Teasers 6

a great new concept

Each book in the FUNFAX series has been designed for you to enjoy purely as a book . . . or, you will find that each page has been perforated and drilled six holes to enable you to remove the pages from this book and place them into your FUNFAX Organiser. If you already have an organiser — they will probably fit that too!!

BRAIN TEASERS

A book designed to test your brain on a variety of subjects. You'll find word games, crosswords and puzzles in this brain-teasing book. If you cannot solve all the puzzles, don't panic — the answers appear in the back of the book.

ISBN 1-85597-043-0

Henderson Publishing
Woodbridge, England

9 781855 970434

99p

How  Works

This book has been designed for you to enjoy purely as a book, or to use in conjunction with your FUNFAX Organiser.

 If you decide to transfer the pages into your FUNFAX Organiser you will notice that each page has been perforated and drilled 6 holes.

Carefully remove the required number of pages. At the back of your FUNFAX Organiser there is a section specially designed to store up to 16 different FUNFAX books.

Write book title in space provided

Place the pages into the rings and write the title of this book in the space provided.